Some Chance!

Brown and Brown

Publishers: Brown and Brown,
             Keeper's Cottage,
             Westward,
             Wigton,
             Cumbria CA7 8NQ
             Tel. 016973 42915

Copyright © Hugh and Margaret Brown 1995

First published 1995
Reprinted 2000 & 2005

ISBN 1 870596 52 8

Printed by Reed's Ltd., Penrith, Cumbria on 100% recycled
paper and card.

Introduction

Some Chance! is a short story in five chapters, written in the first person by four different characters.

There is an accompanying book of photocopiable exercises called **Some Chance!** *Exercises*, which contains 4 pages of exercises for each chapter, and some general exercises to be undertaken after reading the whole book.

Please note: This book, ***Some Chance!***, may not be photocopied.

Contents

1. Shina

I am 36.

I am married with 3 children.

Ravinder, the boy, is almost 15.

The girls are 13 and 9.

Ravi and Lila, the older girl, are doing well at school.

Suki, the youngest, is a problem.

She hates school and she and her friends are often in trouble.

When I was at school, girls didn't get into trouble much.

At least, not at that age.

Mind you, I didn't like school myself.

I wasn't much good at English or Maths.

If you aren't much good at them, it's hard to do well at anything else.

I wasn't too bad at reading but I was no good at spelling and writing.

I used to like history but I couldn't put it down on paper.

I was good at practical subjects - cooking, games - that sort of thing.

When I left school I got a job in my uncle's clothing firm.

He didn't do me any favours apart from giving me the job.

The money was terrible - even for those days.

But it was better than a training scheme.

I was a machinist making overalls.

I was there for 5 years until Ravi was born.

I did lots of different part-time jobs while the kids were growing up.

Then last year I decided to go to College.

I joined this Course called 'Women Returners'.

Stupid name, isn't it?

But it was the chance I'd been waiting for.

It fitted in with school hours, so I was home before the kids got in.

I was terrified on the first day.

I didn't think anyone could be as thick as I was.

It took me a few weeks to realise that everyone else felt the same.

After a bit I started to enjoy College.

When I got home I hated spending time doing household jobs.

Sometimes I even enjoyed doing the College homework.

The kids thought I was mad.

Quite a lot of the women dropped out of the Course during the year.

I was one of the ten who stuck it to the end.

I did drop out for a few days.

My lousy spelling and maths were getting me down.

And I was getting some hassle from my family.

But the course tutor was great and talked me into going back.

I'm glad I did now.

I might not have got another chance.

2. Alan

I am 37.

I work as a lorry mechanic.

It's shift work - mainly lates and earlies, but we do do some nights.

We have to keep the trucks on the road as much as possible.

Sometimes you only have a few hours to repair a truck between loads.

The firm's all right.

I've been with them 10 years.

I get on well with most of the lads and the drivers.

The foreman's a funny bloke.

Most of the time he's O.K. - almost one of the lads.

But sometimes he gets in one of his moods and he's a right sod.

I'm quite proud of what my wife, Shina, has done.

She started at College last year.

I didn't think she would stick it.

She's not been one for books or writing until now.

I was the one who had to help the kids with their homework.

And I've always had to do all the paperwork and cheques at home.

Now there's no stopping her.

The other day, she even told me that a letter I'd written wasn't good English!

We had a bit of a row about that.

After all the years she's left me to do the letters!

It's a bit of a struggle to cope, with just my wages coming in.

She always used to bring in something from her jobs.

Now she's always wanting things for College.

Sometimes she's so wrapped up in her books that she hasn't cooked a meal or done the shopping.

I didn't expect things to change so much when she started College.

But I'm glad she's had the chance to get a bit more education.

It's been a good thing all round, really.

I've learnt to cook a bit.

In fact, I quite enjoy it sometimes.

And the kids help more round the house, with only a few complaints.

'Work experience', we call it. 'Training for life'!

3. Shina's Mother

I am 69.

My husband will be 73 next week.

We have 4 children.

Shina is the youngest.

She's always been a worry to me.

She got married too young.

She and Alan were only 18.

We didn't like him much at first.

He's not from round here, you know.

But my husband gets on with him very well these days.

And at least he's always had a steady job.

Shina never sticks at anything for long.

She's had dozens of jobs.

She should have stayed working at my brother's factory.

She could have been a supervisor by now.

I don't know why she's started all this studying and bookwork.

She ought to stay at home and look after the kids and the house.

Ever since she started College, she's been getting all these fancy ideas.

I expect she thinks she's going to be the next Prime Minister.

Some chance!

It's having an effect on the children, too.

The youngest is quite a handful.

She runs rings round her Mum and she's getting into trouble at school.

They don't let me know the half of it, but I can tell.

In my day, girls were taught to behave.

You were taught the important things - like cooking, knitting and sewing.

Sport and 'brain' work was for boys.

Girls didn't want to go to College and University.

Not in our sort of families.

I blame the television.

4. Course tutor

I am 29.

I've been teaching in this College for 6 years.

When I first started teaching I was terrible.

Now I'm a bit more relaxed.

I enjoy it a lot of the time, but it's a very frustrating job.

You never seem to have enough time to do things properly.

There are too many meetings to attend.

There's never enough money for books.

Students are always wanting to see you about this and that.

No course ever seems to stay the same from one year to the next.

Last year, I was course organiser and English tutor for the Women Returners.

I was forced into it at the last minute.

The regular tutor had been rushed into hospital for a major operation.

She was off work for 6 months.

No one else was free and my course for bricklayers had just been cancelled.

On the first day, I was terrified.

I'd never taught an all women class before.

In fact, most of them were terrified too.

Very few of them had had any experience of adult education.

A lot had hang-ups from their school days.

I was 'teacher'.

They expected me to have all the answers.

A number of them dropped out in the first few weeks.

It was hard not to take it personally.

I felt that I'd failed them in some way.

I think they soon realised how hard I was finding it.

Women are like that.

As we got to know each other, things got better.

By the end of the first term, I was really enjoying it and I think they were too.

As the course went along, there were all kinds of problems.

Sometimes I felt like a marriage guidance counsellor.

Other times I got all the problems with their kids - or problems with money.

It was often difficult to keep them to the subject.

One student, Shina, could take over if you gave her a chance.

She would start answering a question about punctuation and, before you knew where you were, the whole class was discussing the Royal Family.

But they all worked hard - far harder than the younger students.

They really wanted to learn.

Shina's a changed person.

When she first came to the College, she was shy and nervous.

Now she's the life and soul of the place.

I don't teach her any more now, but I still see her about the College and in the refectory.

In fact, you can't miss her when she's in full flow.

5. Shina

I was really chuffed when I got my first Wordpower Certificate on the Women Returners' Course.

I had failed my C.S.E.s when I was at school.

I thought I was too thick to pass any exams.

Wordpower isn't really an exam because it's all done as coursework.

But at least it shows that you can actually do certain things.

In the end, I got two Wordpower Certificates and one Numberpower Certificate.

I found the maths really hard.

I reckon most women aren't good at maths.

One girl on the Course was brilliant though.

She helped the rest of us a lot.

We didn't like the maths lecturer much.

She was a bit stuck up.

She was so good at numbers herself that she couldn't understand how we could be so thick.

I finished the Women Returners' Course last June.

At the end of the Course, we all had to decide what we wanted to do next.

It was really hard.

I would have liked to become a nurse, but I wasn't sure I was good enough.

In the end I decided to have a go at the Nursery Nursing Course.

Two other girls were going on to that Course.

And I've always liked kids - especially other people's!

It was funny starting College again this September.

I was looking forward to getting back and starting the new Course.

But, as it got nearer, I started worrying.

I began to get all the old doubts about whether I was good enough.

Would my spelling and maths let me down?

I nearly talked myself out of going with an excuse about this job I might be able to get.

But then Sasha, one of the girls who was going to do the Course with me, rang up and we met for a coffee.

She'd been feeling the same as me but, after we'd talked about it, we agreed to give it a try.

Once we started the Nursery Nursing Course, we realised it wasn't going to be too bad.

There's a lot of coursework to do and some of it is really boring.

But I'm looking forward to the practical work.

We've only been on the Course for 6 weeks, and already 3 people have dropped out.

One of them has gone down to join the Women Returners' Course.

She ought to have stayed with us because she was no different from Sasha and me.

She could have got extra help from Learning Support.

I realise now that a lot of it is just down to confidence.

I'm lucky, I suppose, because I've always had the gift of the gab and I like to make people laugh.

My Mum's the opposite.

She's always moaning about everything.

My husband, Alan, has helped me a lot.

In fact, it's him who's really kept me going.

But don't tell him I said so!

He's always said that he would like to go to University.

Perhaps one day, when we're really old, we'll both go to University.

Some chance!